All of Santa's elves are
busy at Christmastime,
but the busiest of all
is Little Elf!

Let's go,
Little Elf!

Where is Little Elf?

Little Elf
is helping
in the
toy shop!

Where is Little Elf?

Little Elf is baking
gingerbread cookies.

Where is
Little Elf?

Little Elf
is building
a snowman!

Where is Little Elf?

Little Elf is taking
a long winter's nap!

Where is
Little Elf?

Little Elf
is sorting
letters
for
Santa.

Where is
Little Elf?

Little Elf is wrapping presents.

Where is
Little Elf?

Little Elf
is stirring
Christmas
cocoa!

Where is
Little Elf?

Little Elf is
on the way to
your house!

Let's look for these presents.
I wrapped them myself!